D1530066

Puss in Boots

LANDOLL

There once lived a poor old miller who had three sons. When he died, he left his **mill** to the oldest son, his **donkey** to the middle son and his **cat** and a few gold **coins** to the youngest son, Jack. "How can I earn a living, Puss?" Jack asked the cat.

mill

donkey

cat

coins

"Just buy me a pair of **boots** and a **sack** and I will make you rich," said Puss. So Jack did just that, and the cat put some juicy **carrots** into the sack and waited behind a **tree** until a rabbit came along and hopped into the sack.

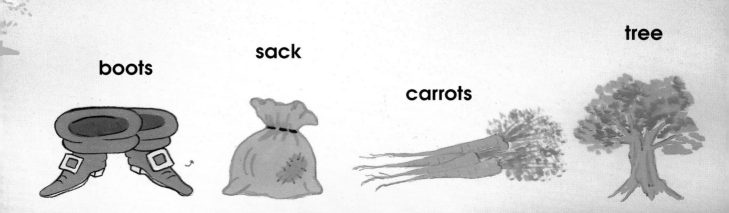

boots

sack

carrots

tree

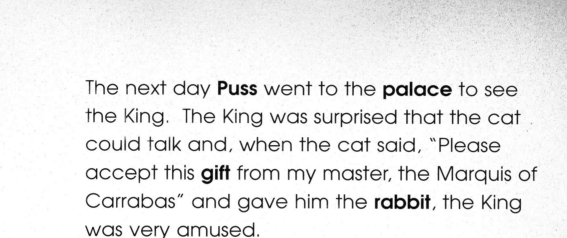

The next day **Puss** went to the **palace** to see the King. The King was surprised that the cat could talk and, when the cat said, "Please accept this **gift** from my master, the Marquis of Carrabas" and gave him the **rabbit**, the King was very amused.

Puss

palace

gift

rabbit

The next day the cat did exactly the same thing but this time he presented the King with a plump **pheasant**. Later that day, the cat returned to his master and told him to go to the **river** near to the palace, and remove all his **clothes**. Then, when the King's **coach** passed, he should jump into the river and pretend to be drowning.

pheasant

river

clothes

coach

"Stop, please help! My master, the Marquis of Carrabas, is drowning," shouted the cat as the **King** passed by with his beautiful **daughter**. Instantly the **coachman** jumped into the river, rescued Jack and wrapped a **rug** around him.

"A thief stole his clothes while he was swimming," said the cat.

"Never mind," said the King. "We will all go to the palace and find some fine clothes for your master."

King

daughter

coachman

rug

Meanwhile the cat ran ahead and ordered all the **farm workers** along the way to shout "Hurrah for the **Marquis of Carrabas**," and, if the King stopped, to tell him that all the **fields** belonged to the Marquis. The cat rewarded them with a **gold** coin.

farm workers

Marquis of Carrabas

fields

gold

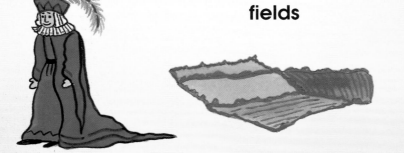

The fields, in fact, belonged to a rich **ogre,** who lived in a **castle**. The cat knocked on his **door** and said, "I hear that you have great powers and that you can turn yourself into anything."

"Of course I can," boasted the ogre.

"I bet you can't turn yourself into a **mouse**," said the cat.

ogre   castle   door   mouse

As quick as **lightning,** the ogre cast a **spell** and turned himself into a mouse. Just as quickly, the cat pounced on the mouse and **ate** it up. Now the castle was his, the cat shouted to his master as the **royal coach** passed by, "Welcome, welcome to the castle of the Marquis of Carrabas." The King was very impressed.

lightning

spell

ate

royal coach

By this time **Jack** and the **Princess** had fallen in love so Jack asked the King if he could marry his daughter. The King was delighted and arranged for a magnificent **banquet** to celebrate the forthcoming **marriage**.

Jack

Princess

banquet

marriage

These are some of the words that you have read in the story of Puss in Boots. Can you find them?

mill	pheasant	ogre
donkey	river	castle
cat	clothes	door
coins	coach	mouse
boots	King	lightning
sack	daughter	spell
carrots	coachman	ate
tree	rug	royal coach
Puss	farm workers	Jack
palace	Marquis of Carrabas	Princess
gift	fields	banquet
rabbit	gold	marriage